THE Woman AT THE Well

EMILY FREEMAN

With Paintings by SIMON DEWEY

DESERET
BOOK

SALT LAKE CITY, UTAH

For Melissa, Sara, Andrea, Amy, Lu, Stephanie, and Michelle

May you be reminded of your own moments at the well,

and of His unfailing promise:

"I will not leave you comfortless:

I will come to you."

—JOHN 14:18

Text © 2008 Emily Belle Freeman
Illustrations © 2008 Altus Fine Art, LLC

All rights reserved. No part of this book may be reproduced in any form or by any means without permission in writing from the publisher, Deseret Book Company, P. O. Box 30178, Salt Lake City, Utah 84130. This work is not an official publication of The Church of Jesus Christ of Latter-day Saints. The views expressed herein are the responsibility of the author and do not necessarily represent the position of the Church or of Deseret Book Company.

DESERET BOOK is a registered trademark of Deseret Book Company.

Visit us at deseretbook.com

(CIP on file)

Printed in the United States of America
Lifetouch, Loves Park, IL

10   9   8   7   6   5   4   3   2

INTRODUCTION

"Early in his mortal ministry, the Savior and his disciples passed through Samaria while traveling from Judea to Galilee. Weary, hungry, and thirsty from their journey, they stopped at Jacob's Well in the city of Sychar. While the disciples went in search of food, the Savior remained at the well. He requested a drink from a Samaritan woman who had come to draw water. Because the Jews and Samaritans were divided by rancor and did not often speak to one another, the woman responded to the Savior's request with a question: 'How is it that thou, being a Jew, askest drink of me, which am a woman of Samaria?'

"In the New Testament the Savior used this simple encounter at the well to teach powerful, eternal truths. Though weary and thirsty, the Master Teacher took this opportunity to testify of his divine role as the Redeemer of the world and to proclaim authoritatively his true identity as the long-promised Messiah.

"These latter days are a time of great spiritual thirst. Many in the world are searching, often intensely, for a source of refreshment that will quench their yearning for meaning and direction in their lives. They crave a cool, satisfying drink of insight and knowledge that will soothe their parched souls. Their spirits cry out for life-sustaining experiences of peace and calm to nourish and enliven their withering hearts.

"The Lord provides the living water that can quench the burning thirst of those whose lives are parched by a drought of truth. As at Jacob's well, so today the Lord Jesus Christ is the only source of living water" (Joseph B. Wirthlin, "Living Water to Quench Spiritual Thirst," *Ensign,* May 1995, 18).

In my eyes, the story of the woman at the well (John 4:5–42) represents the steps each of us must take to receive our own personal testimony of Jesus Christ. I feel certain that many of us experience the same feelings as those expressed by the woman of Samaria. Sometimes when we consider our relationship with the Savior, we may feel we are inadequate or unable to forsake our weakness. We might question our worth and wonder if the Savior recognizes us for who we really are.

We must not allow feelings of unworthiness or inadequacy to hold us back from coming to know the Lord. On those days when we find ourselves discouraged by our weakness, perhaps we could remember this woman of Samaria, considered unworthy by many, who found indescribable solace from a stranger at the well. He invites each of us, regardless of our station in life, to partake of this living water. It is by truly coming to know him that we will find access to this wellspring.

As we learn to communicate with the Savior, he will give insight into our lives and the problems that we deal with day to day. We will begin to realize, just as the Samaritan woman did, that he really does know who we are. Jesus took the knowledge this woman had and added to her faith. As the Supreme Teacher, he built upon her knowledge line upon line until he was able to finally testify that he was the Messiah.

The same is true in our own lives. He will take what knowledge we have and add to it until we receive a fulness of knowledge. He knows us. Just as he knew every detail of this woman's life, he knows every detail of ours. And just as he taught her with the simple analogies that were a part of her daily duty and work, he will teach us in ways that we can understand and learn from. As the Supreme Teacher, he will lead us, line upon line, incrementally, until we finally recognize him for who he really is—our Messiah, our Advocate, our Savior.

Each of us can have the same opportunity as the woman of Samaria. If we choose, we can discover the Savior in the simple, everyday moments of our life. We, too, can drink from living waters.

Are there days when you wonder if you have anything to offer? Have you ever wished there were someone who *really* knew you? Do you long for a closer relationship with the Lord?

Before you begin reading this story, perhaps you might consider this one simple question:

How thirsty are you?

He left Judaea, and departed again into Galilee.

And **he must needs go** through Samaria. . . .

Now Jacob's well was there.

Jesus therefore, being wearied with his journey,

sat thus on the well:

and it was about the sixth hour.

JOHN 4:3–4, 6
(EMPHASIS ADDED)

*T*he ground was parched.

Unrelenting, the sun had baked the earth until tiny cracks formed across its surface. These scars became further proof that the land was thirsty, pleading for water.

Maya kicked up dust as she walked through the fields. The wheat was white, almost ready to harvest. The hot, dry weather had slowly prepared the crop. Soon the reaping would begin.

It was a season of anticipation.

Maya had spent long days working these fields. Months earlier, she had carefully sown the seeds. Then day after day she returned, nourishing the crop, watching the seeds grow and mature.

The harvest would be plentiful, and after the gathering there would be much to rejoice over.

Perhaps then she would be happy.

Clutching her empty waterpot, Maya left the field and stepped onto

the path. The heat from the afternoon sun sweltered around her, and she longed for

the cool, clear water waiting at the well. She knew the rest of the women would gather to the

well at 'Ain 'Askar. But Maya preferred Jacob's Well. It was a much longer walk, but it was worth it.

Maya could not face the women from the town today.

It wasn't what they said, whispering and laughing as she passed by. It was the way they looked at her that hurt the most.

As if she had little to offer.

As if she were insignificant.

As if she were nothing.

Maybe they were right.

Maya came around the final bend of the shaded path leading to the familiar place that had become sacred to her. It was here that several roads met and parted: south to Jerusalem, west to Shechem, and north to Sychar. At the center place stood Jacob's Well.

It was a place of solitude she visited daily, for few travelers came to the well at this hour.

It was her reprieve.

But looking up, Maya quickly realized today would be different. An unexpected visitor, travel-worn and weary, waited there.

*I*t seemed as though Maya would not obtain all that she had come for after all.

The water was a necessity, almost a luxury, at this time of year, and she would fulfill her duty.

It would not take long to fill the waterpot and begin her journey home.

It was the quiet moments of pondering she would miss today—the moments she spent reaching into the deepest parts of her heart to discover what was lacking. As always, there was a longing there—but it would have to wait.

*M*aya hurried over to the well and prepared to fill her waterpot. Glancing quickly at the stranger, she saw he was watching her. He looked as though he had traveled quite a distance, and yet she noticed he had brought nothing to help him reach the cool water deep within the well.

His kind eyes caught her attention as he softly said, "Give me to drink."

In this country, if someone asked for water from one who could provide it, it was customary to grant the request. And yet Maya couldn't help but hesitate.

He was a Jew; of that she was certain. She could tell by the white fringe on the hem of his robe. Why, then, would he ask her, a woman of Samaria, for a drink?

The familiar feelings of doubt filled her heart.

She was not good enough to speak to him. Surely he did not recognize who she was. If he did, he would want nothing to do with her.

It was as simple as this: She was not enough. She never would be.

$\mathcal{M}$aya untangled the cord and began to fasten one end around her waterpot. Watching her own fingers tie the knot, she replied, "How is it that thou, being a Jew, asketh drink of me, which am a woman of Samaria? for the Jews have no dealings with the Samaritans."

For a moment the stranger looked down at his dust-covered feet. Then he lifted his eyes to meet her questioning gaze, replying softly, "If thou knewest the gift of God, and who it is that saith to thee, Give me to drink; thou wouldest have asked of him, and he would have given thee living water."

Maya searched his eyes, trying to understand what he implied. He had requested of her a service, which she had not fulfilled. Now, in return, he was offering her a gift—one that was inconceivable.

Who was this man?

aya sensed a gentleness in his heart. She could tell that he was a man who couldn't help but offer relief, even if it seemed out of reach. But she would not allow herself to trust him. What he was offering was impossible for him to grant. It was like the happiness she longed for—nothing could quench her yearning.

Shaking her head, she reminded him, "Sir, thou hast nothing to draw with, and the well is deep: from whence then hast thou that living water?"

He raised his eyebrows. Thoughtfully, patiently, he considered her. Intrigued but skeptical, she waited.

Finally the answer came: "Whosoever drinketh of this water shall thirst again," he replied, pointing into the depths of the well below. Then he caught her gaze, his piercing eyes reaching into her soul: "But the water that I shall give [thee] shall be . . . a well of water springing up into everlasting life."

Maya quickly shifted her gaze, fumbling again with the tangled cord. It was almost as if he could discern all of the inward wants of her heart, and she wondered if it was more than chance, perhaps even unsought providence, that had led her to this stranger.

*W*orking more slowly now, Maya carefully pondered his reply. Was the water he spoke of the kind that would quench her thirst after a long day in the field, or was it something more? It was almost as if he was reaching into her soul to fill the longing deep within. Could he possibly know her heart?

There was only one way to find out, and so she petitioned, "Sir, give me this water, that I thirst not, neither come hither to draw."

Hesitant, she waited for his reply.

*H*is answer broke her heart: "Go, call thy husband, and come hither."

Leaning against the well for strength, she bent her head, covering her face with her hand so that he would not see the tears. Struggling to regain her composure, she whispered, "I have no husband."

The man pondered her response. "Thou hast well said, I have no husband," came his gentle reply. "In that saidst thou truly."

Maya was astonished.

He knew her.

She did not know how it was possible, but he had recognized her weakness. Somehow he knew personal details of her life that no stranger could have known. He had reached into her soul, revealing the hidden secrets of her heart.

$\mathcal{M}$aya lifted her eyes to meet his gaze, expecting to find the look of scorn she had become so familiar with, but it was not there.

Instead, his eyes held the promise of peace she longed for.

She remembered the words he had spoken to her earlier: "If thou knewest . . . who it is that saith to thee, Give me to drink . . ." And just as she had before, she silently asked herself, *Who is this man?*

With an unwavering gaze, he waited for the faith that would lead to further inquiry.

Finally, she observed, "Sir, I perceive that thou art a prophet."

He slowly nodded, his eyes watching for any sign of doubt.

Again, as it had been when they met, his kind eyes caught her attention as he softly spoke, "Woman, believe me."

What he asked would require her heart. It was something Maya might have considered before she had lost hope. A time, long ago, when she had been happy.

But now?

She had come to realize that it didn't matter how much you believed; some yearnings would never be satisfied. Life had required her to sacrifice her heart's desires. Dreams she had, but would never know.

She'd become used to letting go.

There was only one belief she had never turned her back on. Hesitantly she confided, "I know that Messias cometh, which is called Christ: when he is come, he will tell us all things."

He would be able to explain the hurt.

He, alone, would understand her suffering.

To Him, she would matter.

Of that she was certain.

It was important to her that the stranger understood this. His acceptance of this belief was the only way she could allow herself to believe his words. Maya looked up into his steady gaze, and her heart filled with warmth.

Finally she nodded her head.

*F*or the first time a smile touched
the corner of his caring eyes, and he
replied, "I that speak unto thee am he."

$\mathcal{A}$s the warmth flowed from her heart and washed over her body,
Maya knew what he said was true.

She knew him.

He was a stranger no more.

She fell at his feet and let her tears flow, soothing her parched soul.

Moments ago she had come to the well to perform an ordinary duty.

Unexpectedly, she had been given a gift that would change her life.

For a moment she looked up at him with wonder, and then she stood.

She could not be still any longer.

Her waterpot forgotten along with her burden, Maya ran down the path, through the wheat field, and into the town she had tried to avoid for so many years.

Whether or not she was insignificant was no longer a concern. She had something to offer. Perhaps someone would believe on her words.

And that, in itself, was enough.

With the hint of a smile, he watched her go.
Maya would be a part of the gathering and
rejoicing after all.

*T*he harvest of gladness had come.

Whosoever drinketh of the water that I shall give him

shall never thirst; but the water that I shall give him

shall be in him a well of water springing up into everlasting life.

JOHN 4:14

REFERENCES

Maya

From *mayim*, the Hebrew word for water.

The wheat was white, almost ready to harvest.

"Jesus . . . emerged into the rich Plain of Samaria. Far as the eye could sweep, 'the fields' were 'already white unto the harvest.' . . . All this, and much more, forms a unique background to the picture of this narrative" (Alfred Edersheim, *The Life and Times of Jesus the Messiah* [Grand Rapids, Mich.: World Publishing, 1971], 405, 407).

. . . the well at 'Ain 'Askar.

"There was another well (the 'Ain 'Askar), on the east side of the little town, and much nearer to Sychar than 'Jacob's Well;' and to it probably the women of Sychar generally resorted. This Samaritaness may have chosen 'Jacob's Well,' perhaps, because she had been at work in the fields close by; or else, because, the concourse of the more common women at the village-well might scarcely be a pleasant place of resort to one with her history" (Edersheim, *The Life and Times of Jesus the Messiah*, 409).

It was here that several roads met and parted.

"At 'the Well of Jacob,' which, for our present purpose, may be regarded as the centre of the scene, several ancient Roman roads meet and part. That southward . . . to Jerusalem; that westward traverses the vale of Shechem; that northward brings us to the ancient Sychar" (Edersheim, *The Life and Times of Jesus the Messiah*, 405).

The water was a necessity, almost a luxury . . .

"Water in the East is not only a necessity, but a delicious luxury, and the natives of Palestine are connoisseurs as to its quality" (Frederic W. Farrar, *The Life of Christ* [Salt Lake City: Bookcraft, 1994], 98).

. . . if someone asked for water . . . it was customary to grant the request.

"By the rules of . . . hospitality then prevailing, a request for water was one that should never be denied if possible to grant; yet the woman hesitated, for she was amazed that a Jew should ask a favor of a Samaritan, however great the need" (Talmage, *Jesus the Christ* [Salt Lake City: Deseret Book, 1915, 1947], 173).

She could tell by the white fringe on the hem of his robe.

"Even if He had not spoken, the Samaritaness would have recognized the Jew by His appearance and dress, if, as seems likely, He wore the fringes on the border of His garment. The 'fringes' on the Tallith of the Samaritans are blue, while those worn by the Jews, are white" (Edersheim, *The Life and Times of Jesus the Messiah*, 409).

Samaria

"The direct route from Judea to Galilee lay through Samaria; but many Jews, particularly Galileans, chose to follow an indirect though longer way rather than traverse the country of a people so despised by them as were the Samaritans. . . . In His journey to Galilee Jesus took the shorter course, through Samaria; and doubtless His choice was guided by purpose, for we read that 'he must needs go' that way" (James E. Talmage, *Jesus the Christ*, [Salt Lake City: Deseret Book, 1915, 1947], 172–73).

Living Water

"Do you wish to partake of this living water and experience that divine well springing up within you to everlasting life?

"Then be not afraid. Believe with all your hearts. Develop an unshakenable faith in the Son of God. Let your hearts reach out in earnest prayer. Fill your minds with knowledge of Him. Forsake your weaknesses. Walk in holiness and harmony with the commandments.

"Drink deeply of the living waters of the gospel of Jesus Christ" (Joseph B. Wirthlin, "The Abundant Life," *Ensign*, May 2006, 100).

He had requested of her a service, which she had not fulfilled.

"He had asked her a little favour, which she had delayed, or half declined; he now offers her an eternal gift" (Farrar, *The Life of Christ*, 99).

. . . nothing could quench her yearning.

"Many in the world are searching, often intensely, for a source of refreshment that will quench their yearning for meaning and direction in their lives" (Joseph B. Wirthlin, "Living Water to Quench Spiritual Thirst," *Ensign*, May 1995, 18).

Thoughtfully, patiently, he considered her. Intrigued but skeptical, she waited.

"He patiently, yet thoughtfully, answered the woman. . . . Intrigued but skeptical, and seeing that Jesus had no container with which to draw water, the woman queried further" (Wirthlin, *Ensign*, May 1995, 18).

. . . all of the inward wants of her heart.

"It was not water like that of Jacob's Well which He would give, but 'living water.' But there was more than this: it was water which for ever quenched the thirst, by meeting all the inward wants of the soul; it was not only the meeting of wants felt, but a new life" (Edersheim, *The Life and Times of Jesus the Messiah*, 412).

. . . perhaps even unsought providence

"Both to Jesus and to the woman, the meeting was unsought, Providential in the truest sense—God-brought" (Edersheim, *The Life and Times of Jesus the Messiah*, 409).

Could he possibly know her heart?

"But He taught, not as we teach. And thus He reached her heart in that dimly conscious longing which she expressed" (Edersheim, *The Life and Times of Jesus the Messiah*, 413).

"I have no husband."

"To her reply that she had no husband Jesus revealed to her His superhuman powers of descernment, by telling her she had spoken truthfully, inasmuch as she had had five husbands, while the man with whom she was then living was not her husband" (Talmage, *Jesus the Christ*, 174).

Maya was astonished. He knew her.

"In any case it was an immense, almost immeasurable, advance . . . that of telling her, suddenly and startlingly, what He could not have known, except through higher than human means of information" (Edersheim, *The Life and Times of Jesus the Messiah*, 414).

"Jesus bids her call her husband and return. . . . It may have been to break a stony heart, to awake a sleeping conscience" (Farrar, *The Life of Christ*, 99).

"Surely no ordinary being could have so read the unpleasing story of her life" (Talmage, *Jesus the Christ*, 175).

. . . he waited for the faith that would lead to further inquiry.

"The conviction, sudden but firm, that He Who had laid open the past to her was really a Prophet, was already faith in Him; and so the goal had been attained—not, perhaps, faith in His Messiahship, about which she might have only very vague notions, but in Him. Such faith also leads to further inquiry and knowledge" (Edersheim, *The Life and Times of Jesus the Messiah*, 416).

"Woman, believe me."

"Once more the Lord answers her question by leading her far beyond it. So marvelously does He speak to the simple in heart. It is best here to sit at the feet of Jesus, and, realizing the scene, to follow as His Finger points onwards and upwards" (Edersheim, *The Life and Times of Jesus the Messiah*, 417).

"I that speak unto thee am he."

"It was then that, according to the need of that untutored woman, He told her that He was the Messiah. It was the crowning lesson of that day" (Edersheim, *The Life and Times of Jesus the Messiah*, 418).

"The first full, clear announcement by Himself of His own Messiahship was made by a well-side in the weary noon to a single obscure Samaritan woman" (Farrar, *The Life of Christ*, 100).

She fell at his feet . . . and then she stood.

"Now, my dear sisters . . . [you] are doing the best you can, and that best results in good to yourself and to others. Do not nag yourself with a sense of failure. Get on your knees and ask for the blessings of the Lord; then stand on your feet and do what you are asked to do. Then leave the matter in the hands of the Lord. You will discover that you have accomplished something beyond price" (Gordon B. Hinckley, "To the Women of the Church," *Ensign*, Nov. 2003, 114).

. . . soothing her parched soul.

"They crave a cool, satisfying drink of insight and knowledge that will soothe their parched souls" (Wirthlin, *Enisgn*, May 1995, 18).

Her waterpot forgotten, . . . Maya ran down the path.

"Meanwhile the woman, forgetful of her errand, and only conscious of that new well-spring of life which had risen within her, had left the unfilled water-pot by the Well, and hurried into 'the City'" (Edersheim, *The Life and Times of Jesus the Messiah*, 418).

"Meanwhile the woman, forgetting even her water-pot in her impetuous amazement, had hurried to the city with her wondrous story" (Farrar, *The Life of Christ*, 101).

Perhaps someone would believe on her words.

"And many of the Samaritans of that city believed on him for the saying of the woman, which testified, He told me all that ever I did" (John 4:39).

"Many of the Samaritans believed on Christ, at first on the strength of the woman's testimony, then because of their own conviction" (Talmage, *Jesus the Christ*, 176).

And that, in itself, was enough.

"So we must willingly give everything, because God Himself can't make us grow against our will and without our full participation. Yet even when we utterly spend ourselves, we lack the power to create the perfection only God can complete. Our *all* by itself is still only *almost* enough—until it is finished by the *all* of Him who is the 'finisher of our faith.' At that point, our imperfect but consecrated *almost* is enough" (Bruce C. Hafen, "The Atonement: All for All," *Ensign*, May 2004, 97; emphasis in original).

"[Coming closer to Christ is not] an event, but a process. . . . We will find that he is not only aware of our limitations, but that he will in due course compensate for them, 'after all we can do.' . . . He can save us *in* our inadequacies as well as *from* them. A sense of falling short or falling down is not only natural, but essential to the mortal experience. But, after all we can do, the Atonement can fill that which is empty, straighten our bent parts, and make strong that which is weak" (Bruce C. Hafen, "Beauty for Ashes: The Atonement of Jesus Christ," *Ensign*, Apr. 1990, 8, 13; emphasis in original).

Maya would be a part of the gathering . . .

"These strange tidings soon gathered many around her" (Edersheim, *The Life and Times of Jesus the Messiah*, 418).

. . . rejoicing after all.

"Passing from this point, we notice how the Lord further unfolded His own lesson of present harvest, and their inversion of what was sowing, and what reaping time . . . so that in this instance the sower rejoiced equally as the reaper. . . . Both would rejoice together, in the gathered fruit unto eternal life" (Edersheim, *The Life and Times of Jesus the Messiah*, 420).

The harvest of gladness had come.

"The Samaritans asked Him to abide with them. We know not what passed these two days. The sower as well as the reaper rejoiced, and rejoiced together. Seed-time and harvest mingled, when for themselves they knew and confessed, that this was truly the Saviour of the world" (Edersheim, *The Life and Times of Jesus the Messiah*, 421).

"You talk of there yet being four months to harvest. Look at these fields, white already for the spiritual harvest. Ye shall be the joyful reapers of the harvest which I thus have sown in toil and pain; but I, the sower, rejoice in the thought of that joy to come" (Farrar, *The Life of Christ*, 101).

"Probably the seed sown during this brief stay of our Lord among the despised people of Samaria was that from which so rich a harvest was reaped by the apostles in after years" (Talmage, *Jesus the Christ*, 177).

REFLECTIONS

Have you ever yearned for happiness?

Are there places in your heart that are empty or filled with doubt?

Is there something that you long for that the world cannot satisfy?

Have you ever felt inadequate?

Are there days when you wonder if you have anything to offer?

Have you ever wished there were someone who really knew you?

How have you learned to discover Christ in the everyday moments of your life?

When he comes to offer relief, do you recognize him?

Have you let the Savior begin to help you recognize your weaknesses?

What are you willing to give up to know Christ

Have you placed your burdens at his feet?

When the healing comes, do you remember to rejoice?

What are you certain of about Christ?

What do you know of Christ?

Where is the well that you visit daily?

How thirsty are you?

And so the sowing in tears

is on the spiritual field

often mingled with the harvest of gladness.

ALFRED EDERSHEIM
(*THE LIFE AND TIMES OF JESUS THE MESSIAH*, 420)